CHINA CL

from Cornwall &

An illustrated accoun

modern China Clay Industry

by Charles Thurlow

Contents **Page No.**

First Published 1992 – Second (Revised) Edition 1997

ISBN 1 900147 04 1

Cover pictures:
The front cover is of a high pressure hose working at Melbur pit near St Stephens.
The back cover shows a handful of decomposed granite before washing and the loading of refined china clay at Fowey Harbour.

Typesetting & Design by THE DESIGN FIELD, Truro, Cornwall.

PREFACE

Cornwall and Devon produce up to three million tons annually of chin clay, a fine white powder, for use by the paper, ceramic and many othe industries. China clay is a major raw material export for the Unite Kingdom second only to North Sea oil and gas.

Although historical accounts have been published, the revolution in chin clay technology since the 1950s had not previously been covered except fo articles in technical journals. This is a revised and enlarged edition of book first printed in 1992 and now out of print. The aim of the 1997 editio is, as before, to provide the layman with information about today's industry Since the first edition further technical advances have been made and ar referred to in this edition.

Acknowledgments

The author is grateful to many former colleagues in ECC International fo their advice and assistance in the preparation of this book. Photographs an illustrations are reproduced with the kind permission of ECC Internationa and the map below courtesy of Professor C.M. Bristow and Wheal Marty China Clay Heritage Centre.

Map showing kaolinised areas of Devon & Cornwall.

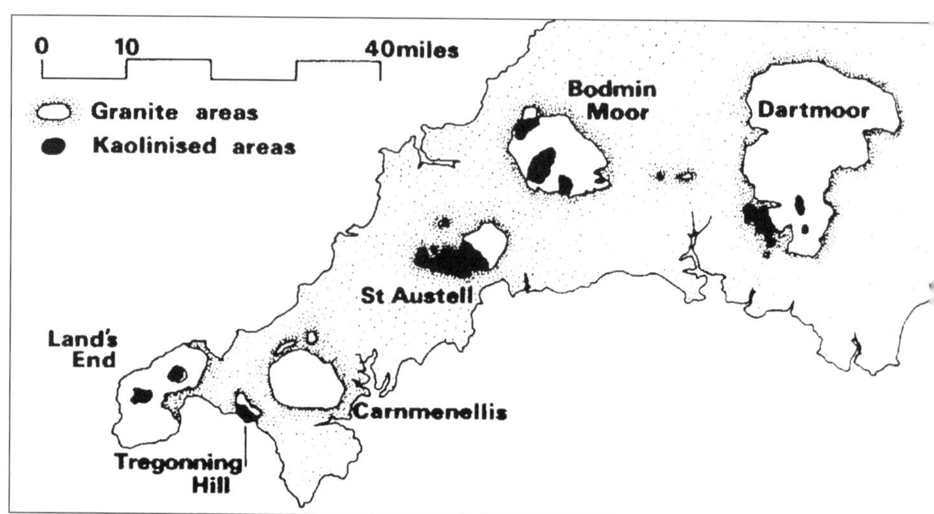

BACKGROUND

Geology

The granite moors of Devon and Cornwall, when first formed about 300 million years ago, contained three main minerals, felspar, quartz and mica. In some parts of this granite the white felspar has since been decomposed to a soft white material. This very fine size mineral is called kaolinite and is the main constituent of china clay. The glassy, angular quartz and the platy silver-brown micas are practically unaltered by the process of kaolinisation but small amounts of fine particle size quartz and mica are also present in the inert, white powder called china clay. A feature of china clay is its extreme fineness. Even the coarser grades of china clay are finer than most talcum powders.

For two centuries geologists debated how felspar was altered to china clay. Two theories were proposed. The hydrothermal theory was that kaolinisation took place as the result of hot chemical laden gases and fluids rising from below ground through the granite soon after it was formed. The other proposition was that china clay had been formed as a result of weathering from ground level at a geological time when the climate was hot and humid. After much scientific research it is now clear that a sequence of events took place which includes both proposed theories.

The hydrothermal action came first and began the alteration process as well as introducing metalliferous deposits such as tin ores and quartz/tourmaline veins which are a distinctive feature of most china clay pits. Tourmaline is a black boron containing mineral. A stage of weathering took place afterwards when water from the surface entered cracks in the rocks. This was warmed at depth by heat due to the unusually high content of radioactive elements in the granite. A slow convective circulation of water resulted which over hundreds of millions of years altered felspar to kaolin. Kaolin is a hydrated aluminium silicate and can be represented by the chemical formula $Al_2O_3 2SiO_2 2H_2O$.

History

China clay came into prominence in the mid eighteenth century, when its value as a component in white porcelain was recognised by a Plymouth chemist, William Cookworthy. He had been looking for the secret ingredients, which the Chinese had used for a thousand years to make porcelain. The amount of china clay produced in Devon and Cornwall gradually increased especially as additional uses were found. The rate of production rose sharply from the mid nineteenth century, when china clay began to be used as a filler in the manufacture of paper on a large scale and received a further boost in the present century, when fine particle size clays found use as a coating for paper.

Several parts of the granite moors in south-west England have kaolinised areas. All of these have been worked for china clay in the past but production is now restricted to areas around St Austell, on Bodmin Moor and the edge of Dartmoor.

The earliest way of clay working was to dig clay bearing ground using hand tools and take it to an area where it was worked with a diverted stream of water. Clay and sand produced a milky suspension. The coarser sand settled out and was taken away in wheelbarrows. The clay was refined in a series of settling pits and thickened in shallow tanks before drying naturally in the open air or open sided shelters called air dries. As

Cores drilled from china clay bearing ground being examined and placed in boxes to await testing.

clay pits developed Cornish beam engines were used to pump from pits and inclined railways carried sand away to tips. Long buildings with heated floors were built to dry the clay more quickly. Some of these methods can be seen at the Wheal Martyn China Clay Heritage Centre near St. Austell.

Numerous companies were involved, working over one hundred small pits and the development of improved methods was slow. During the last seventy years the number of companies involved in the industry has declined, as mergers and take-overs took place. Today all production comes from one large and two smaller companies who operate just over twenty pits, many formed by the merging of small pits. In the second half of the twentieth century, the need for increased tonnages of high quality clay and reduced labour costs led to the introduction of more complex and advanced methods of working china clay. The industry now has the capacity to produce three million tons of china clay per year and the techniques in general use today, are the subject of this publication.

The production of china clay can be divided into three main phases. Clay pits feed raw clay to central refining units where clay is improved to meet customers' requirements and then piped to larger drying plants where it is dried and stored to await distribution.

Prospecting

In former times the existence of clay and its quality in the granite moorlands of Cornwall and Dartmoor, was checked by digging small pits and trenches. This could only give a superficial indication of the amount of clay present.

Today a preliminary assessment is made by geophysical prospecting, a technique where the electrical resistivity of the ground is measured. Kaolinised granite is a good conductor of electricity, but unkaolinised granite is a poor conductor. A survey of this kind indicates where china clay may be found and is also valuable in suggesting areas of hard rock where tips and buildings can be located. Following this, the clay-bearing ground is generally drilled using drills capable of cutting out cores of rock which can be brought up to the surface. These cores are tested to check the quality of the clay and variations with depth. Depths up to 240 metres have been tested in this way.

1. PIT OPERATIONS

Summary

In a china clay pit kaolinised granite is broken up by water jets. this results in a mixture of clay and sand in suspension running to a low point in the pit. The clay and sand are then separated in the pit area. The clay fraction is pumped away for further refining and the sand is taken to tips.

Part of a clay pit showing washing of clay being assisted by a bulldozer.

Removing Overburden

Decomposed granite of workable quality, is usually overlain by a brown stained layer of the same material which is capped by a layer of topsoil. The material, called overburden, has to be removed before the extraction of white china clay can take place. Heavy earth moving plant is used for this purpose.

A shovel loader with a 12cubic metre bucket is filling dumpers with up to 50 tonnes of overburden. Even larger loaders and dumpers are now coming into use.

Breaking up the Ground before Washing

The decomposed granite found in clay pits is by no means uniform. It contains veins of minerals such as quartz and tourmaline and islands of largely unaltered granite. All this material has to be moved, to allow a pit to develop safely. The removal may be undertaken as a special operation or in conjunction with the washing process.

Hard ground is broken up by drilling holes which are charged with explosives and blasted. Holes of 150mm diameter can be drilled with a machine which uses a hard tungsten carbide tipped drill and jointed drilling steels to enable holes with depths up to 15m to be drilled.

Drilling a series of holes for blasting. The rig comprises a compressor and drill mounted on a mast which also holds drill steels.

Ripping

Another method of breaking ground is to use a bulldozer equipped with a steel claw at the back, known as a ripper. The bulldozer alternately uses the ripper to break up the ground and then the front blade to push the broken ground towards the point where washing takes place.

A 500 horse power bulldozer ripping kaolinised granite.

A bulldozer pushing ground which has been torn up by the ripper on the back of the machine.

Washing China Clay Bearing Ground

Water has always been used to break up the decomposed granite. Over the years a special water cannon called a 'monitor' has been developed which directs a jet of water capable of breaking up the decomposed granite in china clay pits. Water pressure up to 300psi (20bar) is provided by large centrifugal pumps, which pump water recovered later on in the process.

The monitor is remotely controlled by an operator from a cabin. The jet is moved so as to maintain a steady stream of china clay, sand and mica in suspension with water, known locally as the wash.

Over the past twenty years, the washing process and most subsequent operations have been carried out continuously throughout the day, night and weekends. This increases the tonnage of clay available and minimises problems associated with starting and stopping the machinery involved.

Right: The latest type monitor has a cranked barrel. This allows rock below the monitor level to be washed more efficiently.

Below: A monitor washing clay bearing ground with a shovel loader stockpiling stent to one side.

The Removal of Rock

As washing proceeds, a pile of hard, unaltered rock known as 'stent', accumulates in front of the monitor. This stone is moved by a rubber tyred shovel loader and taken out of the pit in dumpers to a tip area or may be used in the construction of pit roads or tip foundations.

Gravel Pumping

The wash of china clay, sand and mica in suspension, flows to the lowest point in the pit where it is pumped to a higher level by centrifugal pumps. These consist of a circular impeller inside a circular casing. Wash is drawn from a shallow pond of accumulated material, through a suction pipe, to the

A gravel pump with 250mm inlet and outlet pipes. The design of the impeller allows stones of up to 150mm to be pumped.

Right: Gravel pumps are replaced in houses at the bottom of the pit with a cabin for the pump operator.

centre of the gravel pump. The impeller pushes it through a delivery pipe, which is moulded to the edge of the casing.

Gravel pumps deliver wash to a sand removal plant, often located in the bottom of pits. In some cases, a series of gravel pumps is used to lift the wash to the top of the pit away from clay bearing ground, for the sand removal stage.

Sand Removal

Older methods of sand removal involved settling sand from clay in special troughs or pits and after settling, removing the sand in small wagons. These were pulled out of the pit on inclined railways and tipped nearby. This was a slow and laborious process that was gradually replaced from the late 1950's. Many clay works today use mechanical classifiers that remove sand from the wash continuously and work in conjunction with conveyor belts. Other works use large settling pits where the sand is removed by shovel loaders and dumpers. Conveyors and dumpers allow the sand to be carried for miles if necessary, away from clay bearing ground.

Classifiers and Conveyors

There are two types of mechanical classifier in use today. Both are based on the principle that in water containing a mixture of a sand, mica and clay, the coarsest particles, which are predominantly quartz with some undecomposed felspar, will settle more quickly than the finer particles of clay and mica.

A sand classifier with an inclined spiral taking sand out of a trough. Gravel pumps deliver the wash at a point on the left hand side where the trough narrows.

In the spiral classifier a trough is fed with a constant stream from the gravel pumps. The sand tends to settle in the trough and is pushed out by a rotating spiral 1.5 metres in diameter. Finer particles remain in suspension and overflow the lower end of the trough in this simple gravity settling process.

A more modern device is the bucket wheel desander. A wheel six metres in diameter moves slowly and picks up sand from the bottom of a trough in buckets attached to the perimeter of the wheel. Again finer particles overflow the trough and go to the next stage of treatment.

A bucket wheel picking up sand from the trough. Clay and water drains through the slotted sides of the buckets.

A bucket wheel installation showing dewatering screens and a conveyor belt.

The final section of the conveyor system is a 'spreader' mounted on caterpillar tracks which can tip sand over a wide area.

Sand removed by either method, is placed on vibrating screens, which drain further water from the sand. After screening the sand drops onto a system of conveyor belts, which take it to tips or to a sand grading plant. Sand is carried away from the sand removal process using conveyor belts, made of rubber reinforced with synthetic fibres. A series of belts is used with sand being tipped from one belt to another.

Sand Pits

The alternative to classifiers and conveyors is the use of sand pits where sand is allowed to settle in an enclosed area which is formed by walls of sand and rock and is located not far from the lowest part of the pit. The wash is pumped into these pits by gravel pumps. Here the clay and mica overflow the pits via a vertical wooden launder (pipe). The sand settles in

Sand pits in operation. The right hand pit with a launder on the extreme right is filling whilst the left hand pit is being emptied.

the pit and weir boards are used to gradually raise the height of the launder. A thick bed of sand builds up which, after a period of drainage, is loaded by shovel loaders onto dumpers and taken to a sand tip. Works using this system will have two or more adjoining pits of this type so that one can be filling whilst another is draining or being emptied. This method uses mobile plant occasionally rather than a continuous system of classifiers and conveyors.

Tipping of Overburden, Rock and Sands

The working of china clay results in large quantities of rock, sand and mica being produced as well. Whenever possible, uses are sought for such materials. Most of these by-products have to be put onto tips although there has been some backfilling of disused pits. The ratio of china clay to by-products varies from pit to pit but is generally as follows, giving a ratio of about 1:8

China clay 1
Rock as overburden and stent . . . 3
Sand. 4
Mica. 1

Some rock is sold for use in road construction after crushing and grading. The product, called mica is a mixture of fine sand, mica flakes and some coarse kaolin. The separation and storage of mica is discussed later.

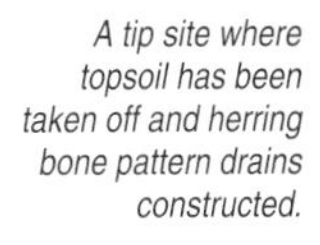

A tip site where topsoil has been taken off and herring bone pattern drains constructed.

About one million tonnes of sand, from china clay workings are sold annually, in total. This sand is used for the manufacture of concrete blocks, general construction and ready mixed concrete. There would be scope for greatly increased sales of this sand and rock but for the cost of transport to more distant markets.

Before tipping begins the ground to be used is checked by trenching and drilling. This is necessary to establish what drainage is required so that water will not build up within the tip. After the removal of topsoil most tips have a herringbone pattern of drains cut into the ground which are filled with crushed stone. Other considerations such as height, slope and volume are planned in advance of tipping.

Tips are built in layers each around 25 metres in height. Upper layers are placed inside lower layers so that the final slope after profiling is much less than the natural angle of repose of the material in the tip.

Nowadays tips are seeded to produce vegetation. This sometimes takes place in two stages. As sand tips develop growth is produced by spraying a mulch containing seed and fertiliser. This controls dust which might blow off a tip in dry weather. Once all tips have reached their planned height the tip is given a smooth profile using a bulldozer to remove the terraces formed by tipping. The tip is then covered with a layer of topsoil, often taken from a new tip site, and seeded. Other schemes include the planting of hard and soft wood trees as screens or general landscape cover.

A tip of rock and over-burden in the background has been profiled by bulldozing. Topsoil is being spread over the tip by a small bulldozer prior to seeding. In the foreground is a modern concrete blocks works which can make blocks at the rate of 120 per minute in a fully automated process.

Separation of Fine Sand and Coarse Mica

The next stage in the process is to remove fine sand and some mica from the desanded wash. To do this, the wash is pumped continuously into a circular, tapered pipe with a maximum internal diameter commonly of 350mm, known as a hydrocyclone or hydroclone.

Left: A hydrocyclone which is one of 20 or more units working together to handle all the wash from a large pit.

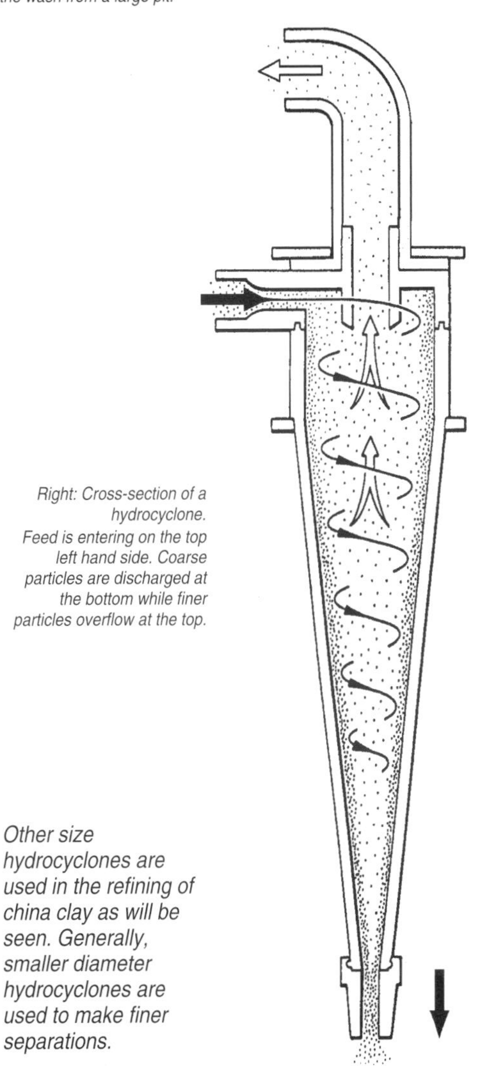

Right: Cross-section of a hydrocyclone. Feed is entering on the top left hand side. Coarse particles are discharged at the bottom while finer particles overflow at the top.

Other size hydrocyclones are used in the refining of china clay as will be seen. Generally, smaller diameter hydrocyclones are used to make finer separations.

The wash enters the upper part of the pipe on one side and swirls around the interior. Centrifugal forces cause the coarser particles to form a layer on the inside of the hydrocyclone and the swirling effect carries these particles to the tapered bottom section of the pipe, where they emerge as an umbrella shaped discharge. The finer particles of clay and mica, less affected by centrifugal forces, are displaced towards the centre of the cone and overflow through a pipe at the top.

The aim in this separation is to divide the feed into particles coarser than 50 microns (0.05 millimetres) and particles finer than 50 microns. At this size there is an almost complete separation between china clay and other minerals, such as mica and fine quartz sand, found in local kaolinised granite. The finer particles are china clay although some further sorting is needed to produce the grades of clay required by different industries. These are pumped to refining plants. The coarse underflow is pumped to mica lagoons.

Pumping Clay through Pipelines

Stainless steel pipelines feeding a refining plant.

Clay is pumped over considerable distances within the Devon and Cornwall clay producing areas. Centrifugal pumps send clay through steel or plastic pipelines, varying from 200mm to 450mm in diameter, so that clay can be pumped from pits to refiners and from refiners to drying plants. Over 200 miles of pipeline are currently in use.

Mica Lagoons

In the early days of the industry, 'mica' from refining processes was discharged into local rivers along with some coarse sand. These effluents helped to form some large local beaches in St. Austell Bay. Today all discharges are contained within the china clay area.

Mica from hydrocyclones and subsequent refining stages, is suspended in water and could cause instability if placed on sand tips. To contain this material, lagoons are formed, with walls built of sand and rock. Some lagoon walls are built around the edge of worked out pits. The mica settles leaving a layer of clear water on the surface. This water is pumped away for reuse. The flat surfaces of lagoons can be restored to agriculture by seeding and careful management.

As new refining methods are developed, early mica lagoons are often re-worked to recover clay which was lost in the less efficient, older processes. This follows the pattern of many mining operations where waste dumps are reworked as technological improvements take place.

Lagoon with walls of rock and sand built round a worked out pit.

2. REFINING PROCESSES

Summary

China clay pumped to refiners contains some finer sand and a small proportion of non clay materials. Refining processes are used to separate out these unwanted components. At the same time clay is sorted into grades of different quality and other processes are used to improve properties such as whiteness and fineness needed by the industries that use china clay.

A control room at a refining plant where instruments used to monitor and control processing are grouped together.

Thickening before Refining

The clay and fine mica which overflow the hydrocyclones, is pumped continuously into the middle of large circular tanks, 43 metres in diameter These tanks are used to remove some water before the clay suspension is refined and have a floor which slopes towards the centre. To assist settling, a flocculant is often added to the clay in the tank. This is a chemical which encourages particles of clay to cluster together, so that they settle faster than individual particles would. The tanks are equipped with two radial, raking arms, with angled blades that revolve slowly and push settled material to a central outlet in the bottom of the tank. At the top edge of the tank, clear water overflows into a channel which leads to a reservoir. This reservoir, called a hosepool, is the main source of water for the pumps that provide high pressure water for washing in the pit. Additional water comes from later stages of the refining and drying processes and from disused clay pits which are used to hold reserves of water. These reserves are especially important in dry summers.

Such thickeners are located close to individual pits. These tanks can be used to hold clays of particular quality. Clay from them is pumped to one of several refining plants and is tested for various properties such as colour, particle size and viscosity. Clays from those tanks can then be blended at the refining stage with a view to producing refined clay of a particular grade.

A group of thickeners withy an enclosed area between them serving as a reservoir for the overflow water.

Refining to Remove Fine Mica using Hydroseparators

In this process, a series of raked tanks similar to thickening tanks, called hydroseparators, are used in a continuous process. These tanks are of smaller diameters, such as 15 or 21 metres. Instead of flocculating the clay fed to these tanks, the opposite process of deflocculation is employed. In this case, the particles in suspension are encouraged to repel each other, by the addition of a deflocculant, usually an alkaline chemical. The effect is that clay particles remain in suspension for some time and overflow the edge of the refining tanks. The fine mica is coarser than the clays and settles slowly to the bottom of the tanks, where it is removed by pumps.

Clay overflowing the rims of refining tanks.

To control refining and blending operations, instruments to measure flow rates, solids contents and chemical addition are employed. All these variables are monitored and controlled from a central control room.

Some clay is trapped with the fine mica, so that the underflow from the refining tanks is retreated two or three times in similar tanks, to ensure that as much clay as possible is recovered. The final underflow from this process is given further treatment.

Refining to Remove Fine Mica using Hydrocyclones

An alternative method of refining thickened clay is to use hydrocyclones. These are similar to those described previously for separating fine sand but are of smaller diameter. To cope with a reasonable tonnage the clay to be treated is split up to feed a number of hydrocyclones. Initially, flocculated clay is fed to hydrocyclones with an internal diameter of 125 mm. The overflow from these is retreated in a smaller set of hydrocyclones with a 50 mm internal diameter. The underflows from both sets either go to a mica lagoon or are retreated in a sand grinding process.

A group of 125mm hydrocyclones.

After refining, clay is piped to further raked tanks for storage. From here the clay will be pumped to a drying plant, if it meets the specification for a particular grade of clay. Sometimes clay from different sources is blended after refining, to match a specification. Alternatively the clay may be processed further, to produce grades of clay with particular properties.

Magnetic Separation to Improve Clays

Refined china clay can include small amounts of minerals such as mica, iron oxides and tourmaline, which all contain some iron. Such minerals can cause specks in ceramic ware when it is fired and will reduce the brightness of clay used for paper making. A powerful electromagnet can remove these iron-bearing minerals from china clay.

Two types of machine are employed. Both machines can use a super-conducting electromagnet to give a high magnetic field with a low electric current This is achieved by having an electromagnet working in very low temperature conditions such as - 267°c. Older machines are being converted to this system.

The machine employed on coarser clays, is a large electromagnet with a circular chamber in the centre, which is 2 metres wide and 500mm deep. This is filled with stainless steel wool. When clay passes through the machine, the slightly magnetic particles are attracted to the magnetised stainless steel wool and held. The electromagnet works on a cycle, with a flushing stage, where the magnet is switched off and clear water is introduced to wash away the slightly magnetic particles, through a separate discharge pipe.

A powerful magnetic separator with a static chamber. Clay rises up into the magnetised chamber and comes out through the pipes in the centre.

To improve fine clays a machine with a pair of reciprocating canisters is used. The canisters are packed with wire wool. They are moved in and out of a super conducting magnetic field. Clay is pumped through the canister in the magnetic field and the slightly magnetic particles are held on the wire wool matrix. After about a minute this canister moves out of the magnetic field and the paired canister moves into the field. The canister outside of the field is flushed to remove magnetics before moving back into the magnetic field. This method allows a continuous stream of clay to be treated.

Fine Clays for Coating Paper

China clay which is to be used for coating paper must be of particularly fine size. To achieve this, refined clay is separated into coarse and fine fractions. The fine fraction will consist largely of particles finer than two microns (two millionths of a metre) in size.

The machine used for this purpose is a centrifugal classifier usually called a centrifuge. Several types are used and one is shown in diagrammatic form below. This consists of a part circular, part tapered bowl, which is rotated at high speed. Refined clay is pumped to the centre of this bowl and the coarser particles move to the edge of the bowl, because they are more affected by centrifugal forces. Inside the bowl is a spiral screw, which is rotating at a slightly higher speed than the bowl. The screw pushes the coarser clay towards the tapered end of the bowl, where it is discharged. Fine clay overflows at the opposite end of the bowl.

This machine employs principles of gravity settling similar to those of the hydrocyclone and spiral classifier, but the high speed of rotation, generates greater gravitational forces and makes a finer separation possible.

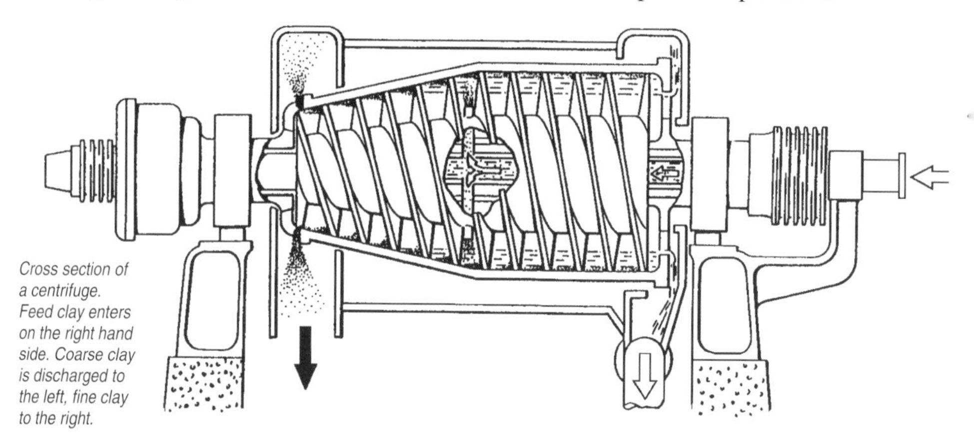

Cross section of a centrifuge. Feed clay enters on the right hand side. Coarse clay is discharged to the left, fine clay to the right.

Centrifuge with feed entering on the right hand side.

A nozzle centrifuge. Feed enters on the left hand side.

Nowadays coating clays with a range of size specifications are produced and other types of centrifuges are used for the finest clays. These work on the same principle but discharge the coarser clays through small nozzles in the bowl of the centrifuge. The bowl speed of these machines is easily varied so that these machines can produce a range of products. In some plants coarse and fine centrifuge products are retreated in other centrifuges to maximise recovery of fine clay or to make clay with particular specifications.

Chemical Bleaching to Improve Whiteness

The whiteness of a china clay sample is measured by comparing the brightness of it, in a laboratory, against a standard of known high brightness such as magnesium oxide powder. Clay brightness is sometimes reduced by staining from peat or by iron oxide compounds both of which can occur in china clay pits.

To improve the brightness where organic staining is caused by peat, china clay can be treated with ozone gas in a very dilute concentration. The gas, produced on site in an ozoniser, is allowed to rise inside a tower. the ozone reacts with the discoloured organic material and oxidises it to a white colour. Any ozone which reaches the top of the tower is detected and burnt off automatically.

Ozone bleaching towers. These contain many small steel baffles to slow down the passage of clay and maximise bleaching.

Staining by iron oxides is more common and a bleaching process using sodium hydrosulphite converts the insoluble iron oxide into iron sulphate. This is less strongly coloured and soluble so that the iron is lost later on in the process when the clay is dewatered. Clay to be bleached is passed through a tower similar to that used for ozone treatment. This helps to remove air trapped in the clay and improves the efficiency of bleaching. The clay then passes through pipework where sodium hydrosulphite is added using sophisticated instrumentation for optimum dosage of this expensive chemical.

Instruments to control and record sodium hydrosulphite bleaching process.

Treatment of Coarse Clays by Flotation

Coarse clay from the centrifuges may be used as a low grade filler or a ceramic clay. Alternatively, it can be upgraded by further processing. The first stage is often to remove small amounts of minerals other than kaolin, which tend to be concentrated in coarse clays.

The process used, known as flotation, is based on the addition of small amounts of chemicals to the coarse clay, which will waterproof the kaolin particles but not affect other minerals. When air bubbles are passed through such a mixture the waterproofed kaolin particles attach themselves to the air bubbles. In practice this is carried out in a series of open boxes, called cells, each of which is equipped with a stirrer which helps create a flow of air bubbles within the cell. These bubbles collect waterproofed kaolin particles that rise to the top of the cell as a froth. Typically a series of six cells is used to treat coarse clay and maximise the recovery of kaolin. The particles which do not float are discarded as mica from the bottom of the end cell.

Several sets of flotation cells with recovered clay froth overflowing. The froth is subsequently broken down by water sprays.

Grinding Coarse Clay

Coarse clay direct from centrifuges or recovered from the flotation process, can be reduced in size by a grinding process. Here it is stirred in hexagonal vessels which contain a special fine sand. This sand is coarser than the clay and when stirred by a rotating agitator in the vessel, breaks down the clay particles. These devices are known as sand grinding machines.

Left: A group of sand grinding machines. Note agitator drive at the top of the machine and ground clay overflowing through screens at the top of the vessels.

Clay is fed into the centre of the machine and after grinding flows out through screens around the upper part.

This overflow is treated in hydro-cyclones, so that any sand which overflows with the clay, can be removed.

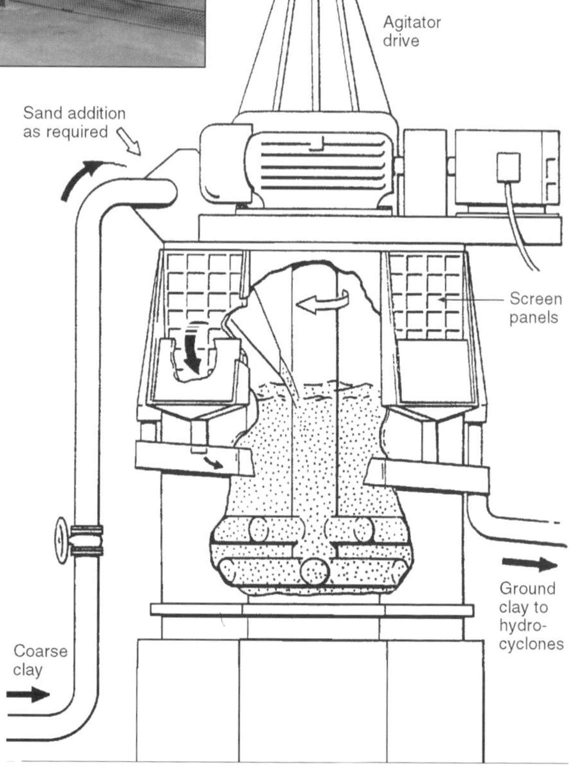

Cut-away diagram of a sand grinding machine.

Grinding Large Clay Particles

Similar machines can also be used to recover clay from the final underflows after refining by hydrocyclones or hydroseparators. This is possible because there are some large china clay particles in this material. Their size causes them to settle with the mica and fine sand in gravity separation processes but they have potential value if reduced to a finer size.

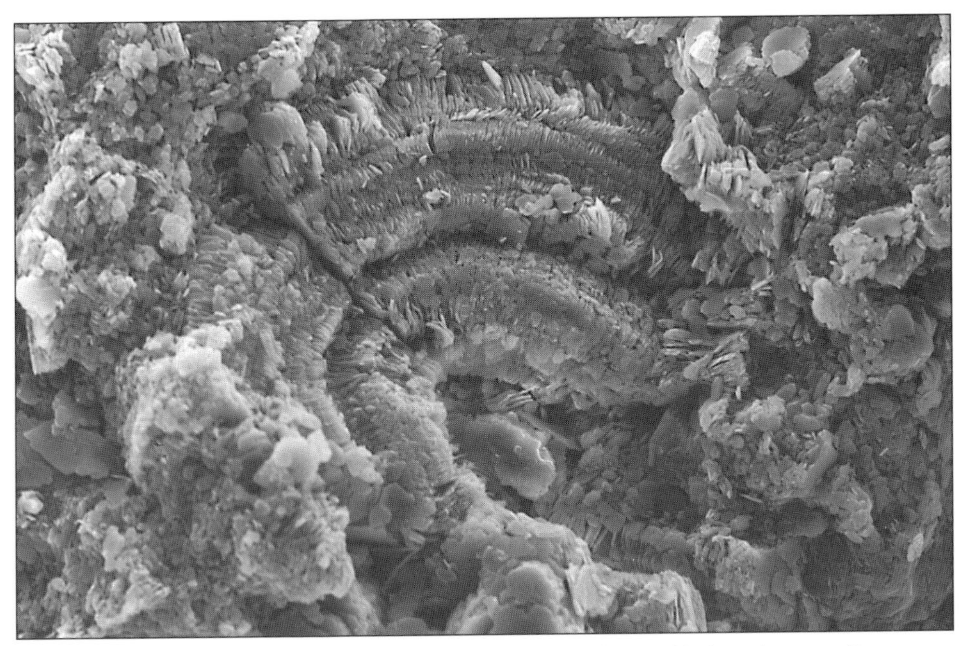

Electron microscope photograph of china clay before processing. The curled stacks of large particle clay can be recovered by grinding which delaminates the stacks.

The grinding process can take advantage of the fact that the china clay particles grind much more easily than the other components. By grinding for a relatively short time the coarse kaolin only is broken down. The ground product is classified in small hydrocyclones to give a china clay overflow. The underflow is pumped to mica lagoons.

Thickening before Drying

In the refining process, some clay remains in a deflocculated state. Afterwards all clay is flocculated by using small amounts of acid, so that the clay settles quickly. This enables the clay to be thickened before the drying process begins, by removing clear water from the top of the storage tanks.

3. DRYING PLANTS

Summary

Refined china clay is piped to drying plants where it is first thickened in settling tanks. This is followed by further thickening in a filter press which produces a solid cake of china clay. The cakes are cut up and fed into a mechanical dryer. The dried clay goes to stores called linhays.

Dryers at Par Harbour showing from left settling tanks, Buell dryers and linhays. On the right hand side is a plant for slurry clay mentioned later.

Filter Pressing to Reduce Water Content

Although clay is thickened in tanks, a further stage of water reduction is used before the clay is dried. This process, known as filter pressing, is carried out by pumping the clay under pressure, into a series of chambers lined with a fine mesh nylon cloth, which will allow water, but not clay particles, to pass through. The chambers are formed by recessed plates, which may be square or circular in shape. A line of plates placed together in a frame, make up a filter press.

Square & Circular Plate Presses

Filter presses with square plates have been used for dewatering china clay for much of the twentieth century. The plates were made of cast iron, but today plastic polypropylene plates are often used. Other modern presses use circular steel plates, one metre in diameter. Either type uses around 120 plates per press.

Filter presses with square polypropylene plates

Both methods of pressing have a similar system of operations, Initially the plates, 'dressed' with filter cloths, are pushed tightly together by a hydraulic ram. Clay is then pumped through a hole in the centre of the plates and clay builds up in the chambers. As pumping pressure is maintained water in the clay suspension is encouraged to escape through the nylon filter cloths where it can trickle out through small passages in the press plate. Thickened clay builds up in the chambers and eventually forms a solid 'cake', the consistency of window putty with a 25 - 30% water content. The circular plate presses produce cakes with the lower moisture level as the circular shape allows clay feed pressures of up to 1,000 psi or 68 bar. to be used in contrast to a maximum of 220 p.s.i. or 15 bar. for square plastic plates. In both presses when a solid cake has built up, after 1 or 2 hours, the clay feed is stopped and the hydraulic ram is retracted so that the plates can be separated. The plates are moved one at a time so that the cakes of clay can be freed. Cakes tend to stick to the cloths, but are easily shifted by hand or by a small pulse of compressed air behind the cloth in circular plate presses.

Filter presses are situated above a system of conveyor belts so that cakes from the press can be transported to the next stage of processing.

A modern circular plate filter press unit showing eight presses with spare press plates in the foreground.

A cake of clay being discharged from one of the presses above.

Filter Pressing in a Tube Press

An alternative method of filter pressing, is the tube press. This consists of two tubes one inside the other, with an internal space between them, except at the bottom where the inner tube is bell shaped to fit closely within the outer tube. The inner tube contains drainage holes and is covered with a filter cloth. The outer tube has a tubular rubber bladder inside it. Clay is pumped into the space between the filter cloth and the rubber bladder. Hydraulic fluid is then pumped into the space between the outer tube and the rubber bladder. This compresses the clay and forces water through the filter cloth. The advantage of this method, is that very high pressures of up to 100 bar, can be used and the filter cake can be reduced to 18% water content. When the pressing cycle is complete, the inner tube can be lowered slightly within the outer tube and the clay cake is pushed off by compressed air.

The product from this filter is hard and easily handled. Clay can be sold in this form.

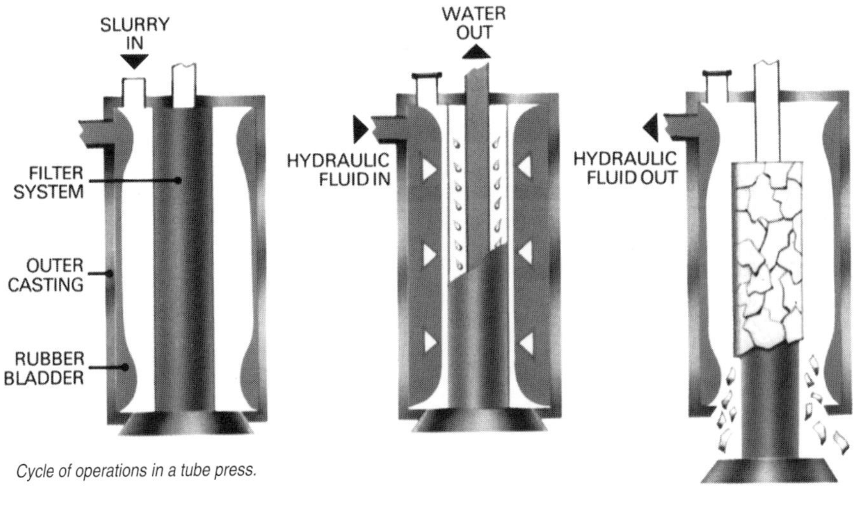

Cycle of operations in a tube press.

Banks of tube presses in the background with filtered clay on conveyors.

Treatment before drying

The cakes from the filter presses are broken up, before drying, by cutting or shearing devices. In addition clays which are to be used for paper coating are often passed through a pug mill. The mill is a cylinder with a spiral rotating inside it. Clay is fed in at one end and forced towards a tapered outlet at the opposite end, where it emerges. The machine is similar in principle to a traditional kitchen mincer. The 'mincing' action tends to round particles of clay slightly and improve their flow properties. This is especially important in a coating clay, where a thin layer of clay in suspension has to flow readily onto a continuous sheet of paper moving at high speed.

A pug mill in operation. Clay is fed in on the right hand side. The steam at the outlet results from the intense 'mincing ' action.

China clay is carried on a series of conveyors to the drying plant. Before entering the dryer, the clay may be put through machines such as pelletisers or extruders to further break down the lumps of aggregated clay particles to a size less than 20mm.

Drying in a Rotary Dryer

The first type of mechanical dryer to be used on a large scale by the china clay industry, was the rotary. This consists of a long rotating cylinder about 2 metres in diameter and 12 metres in length. This contains an inner cylindrical tube, through which hot air from a furnace chamber burning oil or gas is passed. The air returns along a series of flues around the outside of the dryer. Clay is fed into the space around the inner tube and inside the outer tube. The dryer slopes slightly towards the discharge end, so that as the dryer rotates, clay moves to this end, where it emerges from the dryer onto a conveyor belt. The clay, now with a moisture content of 10% is conveyed to covered, concreted storage bays, in an adjacent building called a linhay.

This type of dryer is usually associated with the square plate filter presses, which produce a filter cake more moist than the circular plate presses. Because of this, a small amount of dry clay is mixed with clay from the presses, to feed the dryer. If this were not done, the clay would form into large balls within the dryer.

Rotary dryer showing the discharge end with a bank of square, plate filter presses on the right hand side.

Drying in a Buell Tray Dryer

This dryer consists of a stack of trays in a circular tower, rotated in a current of hot air, drawn into the dryer by fans. There are thirty layers of trays and each of these circular layers consists of a number of radial trays with gaps between them. Clay is fed into the top of the dryer. As the trays complete one revolution, the clay on them is pushed off by fixed arms onto the next layer of trays, so that the clay gradually moves down through the dryer.

Heat for drying comes from a combustion chamber, which can burn oil or gas. A recent alternative is to use exhaust heat from modified jet aero engines which burn natural gas and also generate electricity. The heat is carried by large insulated pipes to the sides of the dryer. A flow of air is maintained by a fan, which draws air from the top of the dryer. This air passes through a special cleaning chamber, where any clay dust present is settled by fine water sprays, before the air passes out through a chimney.

After 45 minutes clay that has been through the dryer emerges from the bottom and is carried away by a conveyor belt.

A Buell tray drier with combustion chamber in the right foreground. A series of inspection doors allow operators to check the trays.

Fluid Bed Drying

Recently introduced into the industry is a dryer in which the hot air for drying in a horizontal cylindrical chamber is introduced under slight pressure through a perforated floor. This has the effect of fluidising pellets of clay fed onto the floor. As a result the hot air is able to dry the pellets quickly and uniformly. The drying cylinder is arranged so that the perforated floor is vibrated in an elliptical motion and the bed of clay is gradually moved across the floor.

Above: On the right is a combustion chamber burning natural gas providing hot air for the fluidised bed. To the right of the drying chamber in the centre, pellets of clay are introduced. these are fluidised and gradually dry as they are vibrated to the left hand side where they discharge into a cooling chamber. This also uses a vibrating fluidised bed with air drawn from the building at room temperature so as to cool the dried clay. Cooling in this way is an effective way to keep dust levels in the dryer building at a minimum.
Note operator looking into an inspection door.

Right: A view through the inspection door of the fluid bed dryer showing pellets entering and being fluidised on the dryer floor.

4. PREPARATION FOR THE CUSTOMER

Summary

China clay is sold to a wide range of industries who use it for differing purposes. Many years ago it was sold as dried in bulk or in barrels. Nowadays it can be sold in different forms and packaging. Some clay is further processed to suit industries with special requirements.

A cylindrical mill for disintegrating clay. On the left hand side is a combustion chamber enabling hot air to be drawn through the mill. Clay is fed into the mill from a hopper behind the cylinder and milled clay is drawn out through the pipe on the right hand side.

The different types of product are:

(i) As dried

Most clay is sold in the form which emerges from dryers or tube presses. This consists of clay lumps, which are formed by the aggregation of the ultra-fine individual particles of clay. These lumps may be loaded directly into road, rail and sea transport, or packed into large bags before loading.

(ii) Milled Clay

Some customers wish to use their clay as a dry powder and for their purposes the lump clay is disintegrated in a special milling machine, which also dries the clay to a moisture content of 1%. The resultant powder is packed into dust-tight paper bags.

A mill for this purpose consists of vertical rotor inside a cylinder. The rotor carries four discs with a series of small vertical blades around their edges. The discs are interspaced with larger plain discs. The rotor revolves at a speed of about 1,500 revolutions per minute and draws in a current of air which has been heated. Clay lumps are fed into the lower part of the mill. The hot air turbulence created by the rotor causes lumps of clay to dry further and collide with each other so gradually breaking down in size. The air current carries this clay up through the mill where further turbulence reduces the clay to a fine powder. The powder is drawn through pipes, by fans, to machinery which packs the clay into strong paper bags and wraps 40 or 50 bags together with a polythene sheet. An alternative route is for the milled clay to be drawn into silos where it can be packed into 'intermediate bulk containers' (I.B.Cs) which are large bags each holding up to one and one quarter tonnes or to road tankers for direct delivery to customers' silos.

Rotor for a clay mill.

(iii) Slurried Clay

Customers in the paper industry use their clay in suspension with water. This has led some customers to buy undried clay in suspension. There is some cost involved in the transport of water, but this can be offset against the handling and power costs, associated with mixing dry clay with water at the paper mill. For these customers, a thick suspension of clay and water, called slurry, is prepared and this can be pumped into road and rail tank wagons, or specially adapted ships.

(iv) Calcined Clay for Speciality Products – Multi-hearth Kilns

If china clay is heated to temperatures above 450°c the crystalline structure of it alters and there are improvements in properties such as electrical insulation value and whiteness compared to the original kaolin. The new properties make the product of particular use in the plastics, rubber, paint and concrete industries. The heating process is known as calcination and some clay is treated to make a range of products by calcining at different temperatures.

China clay to be calcined is usually milled to a fine powder before entering the top of a multi-hearth calcining kiln shown diagrammatically below. The kiln is a large upright cylinder with a series of hearths heated by

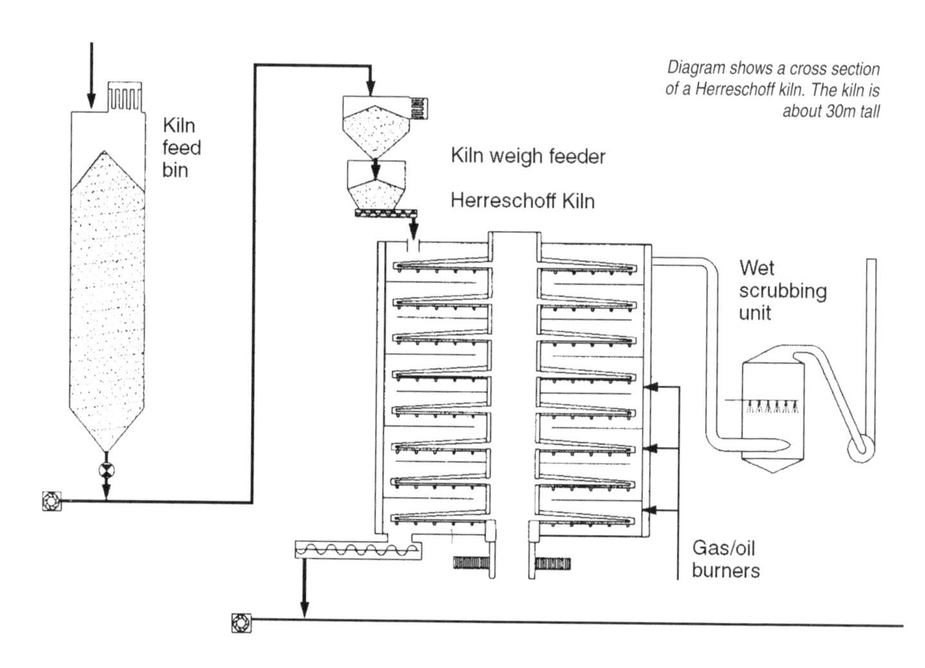

gas or oil burners. A central rotating shaft with arms pushes clay down from hearth to hearth passing the clay alternately inwards and outwards so that after about 30 minutes the clay emerges as a calcined product. There is some fusion of particles during the process so that the calcined clay is milled again to a fine powder for use by the customer. In this type of calciner, known as a Herreschoff Kiln, clay is calcined at temperatures from 500°c to 1100°c. One of the novel applications of clay calcined in this kiln is as an additive for concrete to prevent 'concrete cancer'.

(v) Calcined Clay for Refractory Products – Tunnel Kilns

By heating in a different form of calciner at temperatures from 850°c to 1500°c a range of products with outstanding heat resisting properties known as refractories can be prepared. For this process, long heated tunnels are used.

Clay is dried in a rotary drier and formed, by machine, into rectangular briquettes. These are placed onto flat wagons and put into a tunnel drier for a period of 32 hours at 240°c and then into a tunnel calciner for 48 hours at a maximum temperature of 1500°c. As one wagon comes out, another goes in and wagons in the tunnels move forward. The tunnel calciner has gas fired burners placed on either side. During calcination the bricks are converted to a hard, refractory product. All fired bricks are crushed and separated into different size material. Important uses for this product, trade named Molochite, are for making moulds in the investment casting process and to form the small spacing pieces used to separate china items being fired in a potter's kiln.

An inspection door is open to show one of the arms which moves clay through the Herreschoff kiln.

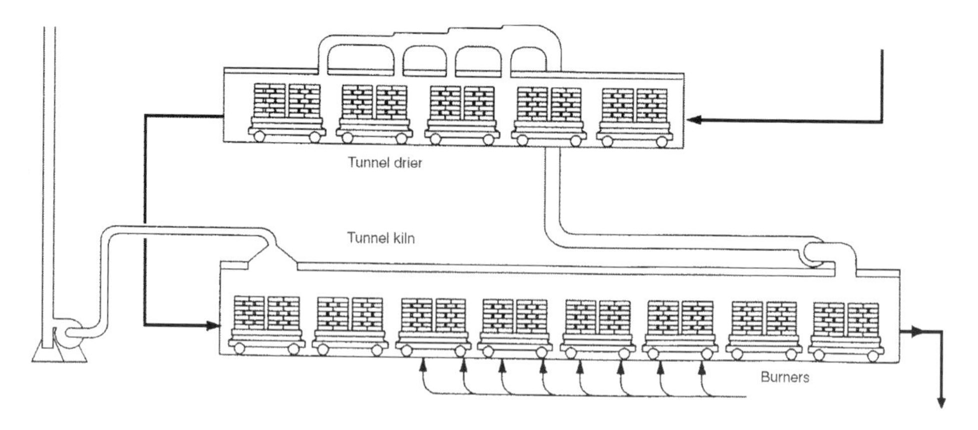

Diagram shows the drying and calcining tunnels. The drying tunnel uses heat from the calcining tunnel.

Briquettes of china clay which have been first dried and the calcined in a tunnel kiln at a maximum temperature of 1500°c. The briquettes are crushed and graded.

Distribution

The counties of Cornwall and Devon can produce around three million tonnes of china clay per year. Well over 80% of this tonnage is sold overseas, mainly to European countries. Clay distribution includes the use of road, rail and sea transport, with stores of clay in this country and overseas, ensuring continuity of supply to customers.

In Victorian times an extensive rail network grew up in the china clay district, to serve the needs of the industry. Although many of these branch lines have since closed, all the modern dryers are rail connected. Just over half of the clay sold in the UK is moved to the customer by rail. Various special rail wagons are used for carrying bulk clay and these are fitted with protective covers to keep the clay dry and prevent loss. A regular rail service carries clay to the Potteries and another service travels regularly from Cornwall to Scotland, carrying slurry clay in tankers.

China clay is usually taken from the storage linhays by shovel loaders and loaded into lorries or rail wagons. A fleet of lorries work in Cornwall within the Par and Fowey harbour areas, transferring clay to vessels at Par or to stores at Fowey. A private road using the route and tunnel of a former branch line, connects the ports of Par and Fowey.

Bulk rail wagons for china clay with bottom discharge doors.

Loading lorries at Par for transfer to stores at Fowey.

Loading one tonne bags in a ship's hold.

A small proportion of clay for export, goes by road and rail, but most is shipped from the ports of Fowey and Par in Cornwall and Plymouth in Devon. Par is a tidal port and can handle cargoes of up to 3,000 tonnes, whilst Fowey has the deepest water and can load vessels with up to 12,000 tonnes. Par and Fowey each hold stocks of clay to enable vessels to be loaded rapidly. The most modern ship loading plant at Fowey, is capable of handling up to 1,000 tonnes of clay per hour. Par and Fowey also have facilities for handling slurry.

5. USES OF CHINA CLAY

To satisfy the varying requirements of customers, over sixty different grades of china clay are produced. The percentage of UK. clay used by different industries is:-

Paper Coating 48%
Paper Filling 32%
Ceramics.......................12%
Other Industries 8%

(i) The Paper Industry

The largest user of china clay is the paper industry where it is used for two main purposes. Relatively coarse clay is used as a filler in the manufacture of paper, to give a smooth texture and whiteness to the sheet. It also helps the paper to take printing ink without the ink spreading, as it would on paper such as blotting, which contains no filler. Papers contain up to twenty-five per cent by weight, of a white powder such as china clay, as a filler.

Fine clays are used, up to fifty per cent by weight, in a mixture with an adhesive to coat paper. The adhesive may be latex, starch or casein. The reason for coating paper which may already be filled with china clay is to produce a smoother, brighter and glossier surface to allow for high quality colour printing. A thin film of coating is run onto the paper which is then dried. After this the paper is 'calendared' by passing it between rollers which can be arranged to give a smooth, matt or glossy finish.

(ii) The Ceramic Industry

The ceramic industries use china clay in proportions varying from twenty to sixty per cent in their 'recipes' for whiteware, which include earthenware, porcelain, bone china, china sanitaryware, electrical porcelain and wall tiles.

(iii) Other Industries

The remaining tonnage is split between industries such as paint, rubber, plastics, pharmaceuticals for uses as diverse as plastic trims for car wheels, fibre glass, pills and electric cable insulation.

Tanker wagons carrying slurry clay from Cornwall to Scotland.

Conclusion

The annual value of china clay sold from the United Kingdom is about 200 million pounds and the industry employs over 3,000 persons. Many other countries have their own deposits of china clay and by 1990 annual world production was around 20 million tonnes. The USA was the largest producer with about 9 million tonnes, followed by the UK with an output of 2.5 million tonnes. The former USSR (mainly from the Ukraine), Germany and Brazil, each prepare about 1 million tonnes.

China clay has been worked in Cornwall and Devon for 250 years and reserves of china clay are expected to last well into the twenty-first century. The largest company involved, ECC International, is also concerned with the working of industrial minerals all over the world. Besides china clay these include, calcium carbonates largely for use in the paper industry and sedimentary 'ball' clays for ceramic purposes.

Looking at the China Clay Industry

The Wheal Martyn China Clay Heritage Centre at Carthew, just north of St Austell, offers a history trail around an old works, indoor displays, a nature trail and a spectacular view of a modern clay pit.